POEMS 1

Michael Harrison and Christopher Stuart-Clark

Oxford University Press

Contents

Can an elephant jump higher than a lamp-post?
    Yes, lamp-posts can't jump.

Why do elephants have big ears?
    Noddy wouldn't pay the ransom.

Why do elephants paint the soles of their feet yellow?
    So they can hide upside down in the custard.
Have you ever seen an elephant hiding upside-down
    in the custard?
    No.
Shows what a good disguise it is.

How can you tell if
there's an elephant in the refrigerator?
    You can't shut the door.

How can you tell if
an elephant has been in your fridge?
    Footprints in the butter.

Knock, knock.
Who's there?
Ivor
Ivor who?
Ivor you let me in the door or I'll climb in the window.

Knock, knock.
Who's there?
Olive
Olive who?
Olive here, so let me in!

Knock, knock.
Who's there?
Luke
Luke who?
Luke through the keyhole and you'll see.

Knock, knock.
Who's there?
Granny.
Knock, knock.
Who's there?
Granny.
Knock, knock.
Who's there?
Granny.
Knock, knock.
Who's there?
Aunt.
Aunt who?
Aunt you glad I got rid of all those grannies?

Knock, knock.
Who's there?
Arfer
Arfer who?
Arfer got.

Knock, knock.
Who's there?
Ken
Ken who?
Ken I come in?

5

Cry baby, cry,
Punch him in the eye,
Hang him on the lamp-post
And leave him there to dry.

If you stay to school dinner
Better throw them aside,
A lot of kids didn't,
A lot of kids died.
The meat is of iron.
The spuds are of steel,
If that don't get you
Then the afters will.

Sir is kind and sir is gentle
Sir is strong and sir is mental.

For what we have put back on the dish
May the school chickens be truly grateful.

For what we have put back on the d
May second dinner be truly gratefu

Tell tale tit,
Your tongue shall be slit,
And all the dogs in the town
Shall have a little bit.

Queen Nefertiti

Spin a coin, spin a coin,
   All fall down;
Queen Nefertiti
   Stalks through the town.

Over the pavements
   Her feet go clack.
Her legs are as tall
   As a chimney stack;

Her fingers flicker
   Like snakes in the air,
The walls split open
   At her green-eyed stare;

Her voice is thin
   As the ghosts of bees;
She will crumble your bones
   She will make your blood freeze.

Spin a coin, spin a coin,
   All fall down,
Queen Nefertiti
   Stalks through the town.

Anon

Four stiff standers
Four dilly danders
Two lookers
Two crookers
And a wig-wag.

Two brothers we are
Great burdens we bear
On which we are bitterly pressed;
The truth is to say
We are full all the day
And empty when we go to rest.

Little Nancy Etticoat
With a white petticoat
And a red nose;
She has no feet or hands
The longer she stands
The shorter she grows.

He went to the wood and caught it
He sat him down and sought it;
Because he could not find it,
Home with him he brought it.

Old Mrs Lazibones

Old Mrs Lazibones
And her dirty daughter
Never used soap
And never used water.
     Higgledy piggledy cowpat
     What d'you think of that?

Daisies from their fingernails,
Birds' nests in their hair-O,
Dandelions from their ears, —
What a dirty pair-O!
     Higgledy piggledy cowpat
     What d'you think of that?

Came a prince who sought a bride,
Riding past their doorstep,
Quick, said Mrs Lazibones.
Girl, under the watertap.
     Higgledy piggledy cowpat
     What d'you think of that?

Washed her up and washed her down,
Then she washed her sideways,
But the prince was far, far away,
He'd ridden off on the highways.
     Higgledy piggledy cowpat
     What d'you think of that?

Gerda Mayer

Through

beside

λ

b

around

bove

BetweeN

Under

neath

10

Christopher Jarman

Weekend in the Country

Robert Froman

ZOOM

ZIP

ZOOM

hONK hoNK hONk Honk HONk honK honK honK hoNk hONk honK HOnk hOnk hONK HOnk Honk HonK hOnk HONk hOnK honK hoNK HonK HoNK HONk honK hONK hOnk

MURDER BLARE HOWL GROAN ROAR SCREECH SHRIEK SCREAM BELLOW QUEAL

FROM HERE TO THERE.

A FROZEN LEAP ACROSS THE WATER

Robert Froman

Sky Day Dream

WITH THEM

COULD FLY OFF

I WISHED THAT I

INTO THE SKY

FLY OFF

SOME CROWS

ONCE I SAW

Robert Froman

ladles and JellyspoonS,
i stand upon this speech to make a platforM,
the train I arrived in has not yet comE,
so I took a bus and walkeD.
i come before you to stand behind yoU
and tell you somethinG
i know nothing abouT.

one fine day in the middle of the nighT,
two dead men got up to fighT,
back to back they faced each otheR,
drew their swords and shot each otheR.
a paralysed donkey passing bY
kicked a blind man in the eyE,
knocked him through a nine inch walL,
into a dry ditch and drowned them alL.

Don't Forget the Bacon!

Six farm eggs, a cake for tea, a pound of pears,
and don't forget the bacon.

Six fat legs, a cake for tea, a pound of pears
and don't forget the bacon.
Six fat legs, a cape for me, a pound of pears
and don't forget the bacon.
Six fat legs, a cape for me, a flight of stairs
and don't forget the bacon.
Six clothes pegs, a cape for me, a flight of stairs
and don't forget the bacon.
Six clothes pegs, a rake for leaves, a flight of stairs
and don't forget the bacon.
Six clothes pegs, a rake for leaves, a pile of chairs
and don't forget the bacon.

Six clothes pegs, a rake for leaves, and a pile of chairs, please.

A pile of chairs? A flight of stairs? – A POUND OF PEARS!
A rake for leaves? A cape for me? – A CAKE FOR TEA!
Six clothes pegs? Six fat legs? – SIX FARM EGGS!

*   *   *   *   *

Six farm eggs, a cake for tea, and a pound of pears

I FORGOT THE BACON

Pat Hutchins

I'm just going out for a moment
Why?

To make a cup of tea.
Why?

Because I'm thirsty.
Why?

Because it's hot.
Why?

Because the sun's shining.
Why?

Because it's summer.
Why?

Because that's when it is.
Why?

Why don't you stop saying why?
Why?

Tea-time why.
High-time-you-stopped-saying-why time.
What?

Michael Rosen

Rabbiting On

Where did you go?
Oh . . . nowhere much.

What did you see?
Oh . . . rabbits and such.

Rabbits? What else?
Oh . . . a rabbit hutch.

What sort of rabbits?
What sort? Oh . . . small.

What sort of hutch?
Just a hutch, that's all.

But what did it look like?
Like a rabbit hutch.

Well, what was in it?
Small rabbits and such.

I worried about you
While you were gone.

*Why don't you stop
Rabbiting on?*

Kit Wright

twould be nice to be
an apostrophe
floating
above an s
hovering
like a paper kite
in between the its
eavesdropping, tiptoeing
high above the thats
an inky comet
spiralling
the highest tossed
of hats

Roger McGough

End of a Girl's First Tooth

Once she'd a tooth that wiggled;
Now she's a gap that lisps.
For weeks she could only suck lollies;
Now she champs peanuts and crithsps.

Roy Fuller

Ice-cream Poem

The chiefest of young Ethel's vices
Was eating multitudes of ices.

Whene'er the ice-van's booming tinkle
Was heard, Eth ran out in a twinkle,

And gorged herself on large 'Vanilla';
Her Mum foretold that it would kill 'er.

No tears could thaw her; once she ran
Away, and hid inside the van,

And promptly froze upon the spot
Like the saltpillar wife of Lot.

Poor Eth is licked! Behold the follies
Of one whose lolly went on lollies.

Gerda Mayer

Down at the Swimming Pool

Down at the swimming pool,
Kenny did a frog's hop,
Dave did a double dive,
And Peter did a belly-flop.

Bob sat in his bath at home,
Soaping sponge and flannel.
Said: *I'm working up towards
Swimming the English Channel.*

Gerda Mayer

Wink

I took 40 winks
yesterday afternoon
and another 40 today.
In fact I get through
about 280 winks a week.
Which is about 14,560
winks a year.
(The way I'm going on
I'll end up looking like a wink)

Roger McGough

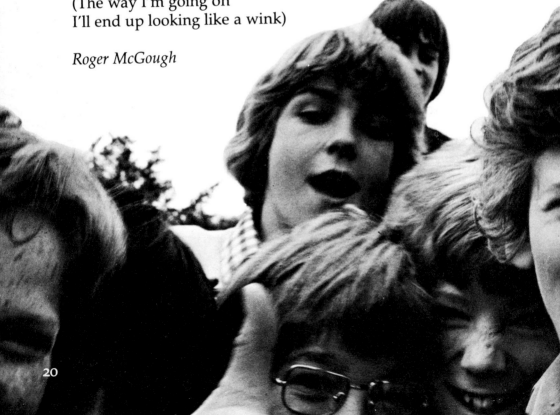

Duchess's Song

Speak roughly to your little boy,
   And beat him when he sneezes:
He only does it to annoy,
   Because he knows it teases.

Lewis Carroll

I am Rose

I am Rose my eyes are blue
I am Rose and who are you?
I am Rose and when I sing
I am Rose like anything.

Gertrude Stein

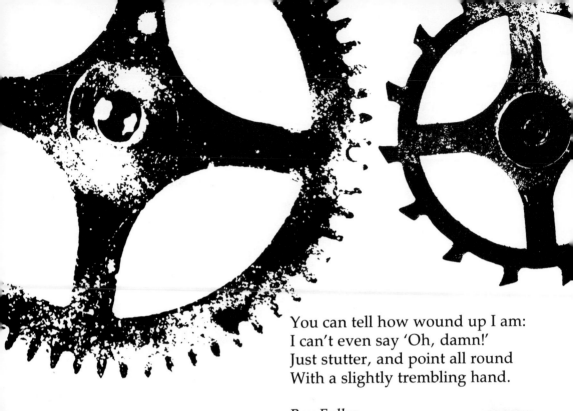

You can tell how wound up I am:
I can't even say 'Oh, damn!'
Just stutter, and point all round
With a slightly trembling hand.

Roy Fuller

'Full, over-full is my heart:
 Please take me away.'
'We'll send a dirty cart
 Every week. OK?'

Roy Fuller

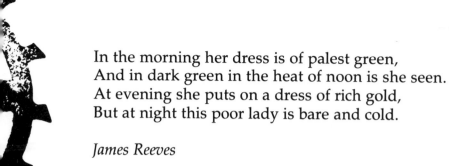

In the morning her dress is of palest green,
And in dark green in the heat of noon is she seen.
At evening she puts on a dress of rich gold,
But at night this poor lady is bare and cold.

James Reeves

Wind in March:
No leaves left
For its stiff summons.

We are very little creatures,
All of different voice and features;
One of us in *glass* is set,
One of us you'll find in *jet*.
T'other you may see in *tin*,
And the fourth a *box* within.
If the fifth you should pursue,
It can never fly from *you*.

Jonathan Swift

Too dense to have a door,
Window or fireplace or a floor,
They saw this cottage up,
Huge bricks of grass, clover and buttercup
Carting to byre and stable,
Where cow and horse will eat wall, roof and gable.

Andrew Young

Hard and black is my home,
Hard as a rock and black as night.
Scarlet and gold am I,
Delicate, warm and bright.

For long years I lie,
A prisoner in the dark,
Till at last I break my fetters
In a rush of flame and spark.

First tree and then a rock
The house where I sleep.
Now like a demon
I crackle and hiss and leap.

James Reeves

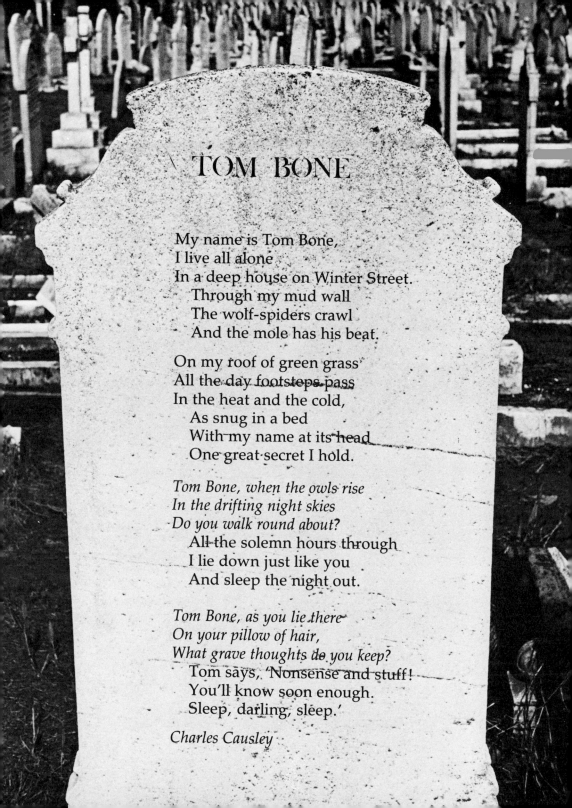

TOM BONE

My name is Tom Bone,
I live all alone
In a deep house on Winter Street.
  Through my mud wall
  The wolf-spiders crawl
  And the mole has his beat.

On my roof of green grass
All the day footsteps pass
In the heat and the cold,
  As snug in a bed
  With my name at its head
  One great secret I hold.

Tom Bone, when the owls rise
In the drifting night skies
Do you walk round about?
  All the solemn hours through
  I lie down just like you
  And sleep the night out.

Tom Bone, as you lie there
On your pillow of hair,
What grave thoughts do you keep?
  Tom says, 'Nonsense and stuff!
  You'll know soon enough.
  Sleep, darling, sleep.'

Charles Causley

The Two Old Women of Mumbling Hill

The two old trees on Mumbling Hill,
They whisper and chatter and never keep still.
What do they say as they lean together
In rain or sunshine or windy weather?

There were two women lived near the hill,
And they used to gossip as women will
Of friends and neighbours, houses and shops,
Weather and trouble and clothes and crops.

And one sad winter they both took ill,
The two old women of Mumbling Hill.
They were bent and feeble and wasted away
And both of them died on the selfsame day.

Now the ghosts of the women of Mumbling Hill,
They started to call out loud and shrill,
'Where are the tales we used to tell,
And where is the talking we loved so well?'

Side by side stood the ghosts until
They both took root on Mumbling Hill;
And they turned to trees, and they slowly grew,
Summer and winter the long years through.

In the winter the bare boughs creaked and cried,
In summer the green leaves whispered and sighed,
And still they talk of fine and rain,
Storm and sunshine, comfort and pain.

The two old trees of Mumbling Hill,
They whisper and chatter and never keep still.
What do they say as they lean together
In rain or sunshine or windy weather?

James Reeves

Small, Smaller

I thought that I knew all there was to know
Of being small, until I saw once, black against the snow,
A shrew, trapped in my footprint, jump and fall
And jump again and fall, the hole too deep, the walls too
    tall.

Russell Hoban

The Fly

How large unto the tiny fly
    Must little things appear!—
A rosebud like a feather bed,
    Its prickle like a spear;

A dewdrop like a looking-glass,
    A hair like golden wire;
The smallest grain of mustard-seed
    As fierce as coals of fire;

A loaf of bread, a lofty hill;
    A wasp, a cruel leopard;
And specks of salt as bright to see
    As lambskins to a shepherd.

Walter de la Mare

The Bells of Heaven

'Twould ring the bells of Heaven
The wildest peal for years,
If Parson lost his senses
And people came to theirs,
And he and they together
Knelt down with angry prayers
For tamed and shabby tigers
And dancing dogs and bears,
And wretched, blind pit ponies,
And little hunted hares.

Ralph Hodgson

Take One Home for the Kiddies

On shallow straw, in shadeless glass,
Huddled by empty bowls, they sleep:
No dark, no dam, no earth, no grass –
Mam, get us one of them to keep.

Living toys are something novel,
But it soon wears off somehow.
Fetch the shoebox, fetch the shovel –
Mam, we're playing funerals now.

Philip Larkin

Wasp in May
Storing his venom
For a long summer.

29

In the daytime I am Rob Roy and a tiger
In the daytime I am Marco Polo
          I chase bears in Bricket Wood
In the daytime I am the Tower of London
          nothing gets past me
          when it's my turn
          in Harrybo's hedge
In the daytime I am Henry the fifth and Ulysses
          and I tell stories
          that go on for a whole week
          if I want.
At night in the dark
          when I've shut the front room door
          I try and
          get up the stairs across the landing
          into bed and under the pillow
          without breathing once.

Michael Rosen

The Dark

I feared the darkness as a boy;
And if at night I had to go
Upstairs alone I'd make a show
Of carrying on with those below
A dialogue of shouts and 'whats?'
So they'd be sure to save poor Roy
Were he attacked by vampire bats.

Or thugs or ghosts. But far less crude
Than criminal or even ghost
Behind a curtain or a post
Was what I used to dread the most –
The always-unseen bugaboo
Of black-surrounded solitude.
I dread it still at sixty-two.

Roy Fuller

The Man who Wasn't There

Yesterday upon the stair
I met a man who wasn't there;
He wasn't there again today,
I wish, I wish, he'd go away.

I've seen his shapeless shadow-coat
Beneath the stairway, hanging about;
And outside, muffled in a cloak
The same colour as the dark;

I've seen him in a black, black suit
Shaking, under the broken light;
I've seen him swim across the floor
And disappear beneath the door;

And once, I almost heard his breath
Behind me, running up the path:
Inside, he leant against the wall,
And turned . . . and was no one at all.

Yesterday upon the stair
I met a man who wasn't there;
He wasn't there again today,
I wish, I wish, he'd go away.

Brian Lee

Goodbat Nightman

God bless all policemen
and fighters of crime,
May thieves go to jail
for a very long time.

They've had a hard day
helping clean up the town,
Now they hang from the mantelpiece
both upside down.

A glass of warm blood
and then straight up the stairs,
Batman and Robin
are saying their prayers.

They've locked all the doors
and they've put out the bat,
Put on their batjamas
(They like doing that)

They've filled their batwater-bottles
made their batbeds,
With two springy battresses
for sleepy batheads.

They're closing red eyes
and they're counting black sheep,
Batman and Robin
are falling asleep.

Roger McGough

The Bat

By day the bat is cousin to the mouse.
He likes the attic of an ageing house.

His fingers make a hat about his head.
His pulse is so slow we think him dead.

He loops in crazy figures half the night
Among the trees that face the corner light.

But when he brushes up against a screen,
We are afraid of what our eyes have seen:

For something is amiss or out of place
When mice with wings can wear a human face.

Theodore Roethke

The dinosaurs are not all dead.
I saw one raise its iron head
To watch me walking down the road
Beyond our house today.
Its jaws were dripping with a load
Of earth and grass that it had cropped.
It must have heard me where I stopped,
Snorted white steam my way,
And stretched its long neck out to see,
And chewed, and grinned quite amiably.

Charles Malam

36

Motorway

Motorway – motorway – motorway,
Never stay – never stay – never stay,
Broad bridge ribbon overrides us,
Giant-strides us,
Manmade dinosaurus, dwarfs us.

Motor-metal fleas fly by,
Whining car horns grow and die,
Skim the giant's broad black back,
White line,
Sign post,
Motor track.

Listen in your sleep, dream deep,
Hear him stamp his giant feet,
Beating, beating, street on street,
Motorway – motorway – motorway.

Marian Lines

Carbreakers

There's a graveyard in our street
But it's not for putting people in;
The bodies that they bury here
Are made of steel and paint and tin.

The people come and leave their wrecks
For crunching in the giant jaws
Of a great hungry car machine,
That lives on bonnets, wheels and doors.

When I pass by the yard at night,
I sometimes think I hear a sound
Of ghostly horns that moan and whine,
Upon that metal graveyard mound.

Marian Lines

It's a Lean Car

It's a lean car . . . a long legged dog of a car
   a grey ghost eagle car.
The feet of it eat the dirt of a road . . . the wings of it
   eat the hills.

Carl Sandburg

February evening:
A cold puddle of petrol
Makes its own rainbow.

39

Sea-wash

The sea-wash never ends.
The sea-wash repeats, repeats.
Only old songs? Is that all the sea knows?
       Only the old strong songs?
       Is that all?
The sea-wash repeats, repeats.

Carl Sandburg

The Tide in the River

   The tide in the river,
   The tide in the river,
The tide in the river runs deep,
   I saw a shiver
   Pass over the river
As the tide turned in its sleep.

Eleanor Farjeon

Moved

The great sea stirs me.
The great sea sets me adrift,
it sways me like the weed
on a river-stone.

The sky's height stirs me.
The strong wind blows through my mind.
It carries me with it,
so I shake with joy.

Uvavnuk

Beach of Stones

That stadium of roaring stones,
The suffering. O they are not dumb things,
Though bleached and worn, when water
Strikes at them. Stones will be the last ones;
They are earth's bones, no easy prey
For breakers. And they are not broken
But diminish only, under the pestle,
Under protest. They shift through centuries,
Grinding their way towards silence.

Kevin Crossley-Holland

Morning in June:
On the sea's horizon
A white island, alone.

Washing-up Song

Chip the glasses and crack the plates!
  Blunt the knives and bend the forks!
That's what Bilbo Baggins hates –
  Smash the bottles and burn the corks!

Cut the cloth and tread on the fat!
  Pour the milk on the pantry floor!
Leave the bones on the bedroom mat!
  Splash the wine on every door!

Dump the crocks in a boiling bowl;
  Pound them up with a thumping pole;
And when you've finished, if any are whole,
Send them down the hall to roll!

That's what Bilbo Baggins hates!
So, carefully! carefully with the plates!

J. R. R. Tolkien

Sink Song

Scouring out the porridge pot,
  Round and round and round!

Out with all the scraith and scoopery,
Lift the eely ooly droopery,
Chase the glubbery slubbery gloopery
  Round and round and round!

Out with all the doleful dithery,
  Ladle out the slimy slithery,
Hunt and catch the hithery thithery,
  Round and round and round!

Out with all the obbly gubbly,
On the stove it burns so bubbly,
Use the spoon and use it doubly,
  Round and round and round!

J. A. Lindon

NO!

No sun – no moon!
No morn – no noon –
No dawn – no dusk – no proper time of day –
    No sky – no earthly view –
    No distance looking blue –
No road – no street – no 't'other side the way' –
    No end to any Row –
    No indications where the Crescents go –
    No top to any steeple –
No recognitions of familiar people –
    No courtesies for showing 'em –
    No knowing 'em! –
No travelling at all – no locomotion,
No inkling of the way – no notion –
    'No go' – by land or ocean –
    No mail – no post –
No news from any foreign coast –
No Park – no Ring – no afternoon gentility –
    No company – no nobility –
No warmth, no cheerfulness, no healthful ease,
    No comfortable feel in any member –
No shade, no shine, no butterflies, no bees,
    No fruits, no flowers, no leaves, no birds, –
November!

Thomas Hood

from The Cataract of Lodore

The Cataract strong
Then plunges along,
Striking and raging
As if a war waging
Its caverns and rocks among:
Rising and leaping,
Sinking and creeping,
Swelling and sweeping,
Showering and springing,
Flying and flinging,
Writhing and ringing,
Eddying and whisking,
Spouting and frisking,
Turning and twisting,
Around and around
With endless rebound!
Smiting and fighting,
A sight to delight in;
Confounding, astounding,
Dizzying and deafening the ear with its sound.

Dividing and gliding and sliding,
And falling and brawling and sprawling,
And driving and riving and striving,
And sprinkling and twinkling and wrinkling,
And sounding and bounding and rounding,
And bubbling and troubling and doubling,
And grumbling and rumbling and tumbling,
And clattering and battering and shattering;
Retreating and beating and meeting and sheeting,
Delaying and straying and playing and spraying,
Advancing and prancing and glancing and dancing,
Recoiling, turmoiling and toiling and boiling,
And gleaming and streaming and steaming and beaming,
And rushing and flushing and brushing and gushing,
And flapping and rapping and clapping and slapping,
And curling and whirling and purling and twirling,
And thumping and plumping and bumping and jumping,
And dashing and flashing and splashing and clashing;
And so never ending, but always descending,
Sounds and motions for ever and ever are blending,
All at once and all o'er, with a mighty uproar,
And this way the Water comes down at Lodore.

Robert Southey

My dad's thumb
can stick pins in wood
without flinching –
it can crush family-size matchboxes
in one stroke
and lever off jam-jar lids without piercing
at the pierce here sign.

If it wanted
it could be a bath-plug
or a paint-scraper
a keyhole cover or a tap-tightener.

It's already a great nutcracker
and if it dressed up
it could easily pass
as a broad bean or a big toe.

Father says   In actual fact, it's quite simply
Never   the world's fastest envelope burster.
let
me   *Michael Rosen*
see
you
doing
that
again
father says
tell you once
tell you a thousand times
come hell or high water
his finger drills my shoulder
never let me see you doing that again

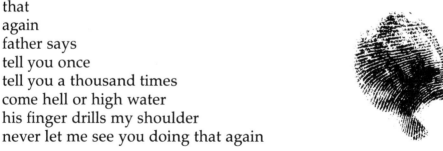

My brother knows all his phrases off by heart
so we practise them in bed at night.

Michael Rosen

My Dad, Your Dad

My dad's fatter than your dad,
Yes, my dad's fatter than yours:
If he eats any more he won't fit in the house,
He'll have to live out of doors.

Yes, but my dad's balder than your dad,
My dad's balder, O.K.,
He's only got two hairs left on his head
And both are turning grey.

Ah, but my dad's thicker than your dad,
My dad's thicker, all right.
He has to look at his watch to see
If it's noon or the middle of the night.

Yes, but my dad's more boring than your dad.
If he ever starts counting sheep
When he can't get to sleep at night, he finds
It's the sheep that go to sleep.

But my dad doesn't mind your dad.
Mine quite likes yours too.
I suppose they don't always think much of US!
That's true, I suppose, that's true.

Kit Wright

My Father

Some fathers work at the office, others work at the store,
Some operate great cranes and build up skyscrapers galore,
Some work in canning factories counting green peas into cans,
Some drive all night in huge and thundering removal vans.

    But mine has the strangest job of the lot.
    My Father's the Chief Inspector of –
      What?
    O don't tell the mice, don't tell the moles,
    My Father's the Chief Inspector of
      HOLES.

It's a work of the highest importance because you never know
What's in a hole, what fearful thing is creeping from below.
Perhaps it's a hole to the ocean and will soon gush water in tons,
Or maybe it leads to a vast cave full of gold and skeletons.

    Though a hole might seem to have nothing but dirt in,
    Somebody's simply got to make certain.
    Caves in the mountain, clefts in the wall,
    My Father has to inspect them all.

That crack in the road looks harmless. My Father knows it's not.
The world may be breaking into two and starting at that spot.
Or maybe the world is a great egg, and we live on the shell,
And it's just beginning to split and hatch: you simply cannot tell.

If you see a crack, run to the phone, run!
My Father will know just what's to be done.
A rumbling hole, a silent hole,
My Father will soon have it under control.

Keeping a check on all these holes he hurries from morning to night.
There might be sounds of marching in one, or an eye shining bright.
A tentacle came groping from a hole that belonged to a mouse,
A floor collapsed and Chinamen swarmed up into the house.

A Hole's an unpredictable thing –
Nobody knows what a Hole might bring.
Caves in the mountain, clefts in the wall,
My Father has to inspect them all!

Ted Hughes

Mr Tom Narrow

A scandalous man
    Was Mr Tom Narrow,
He pushed his grandmother
    Round in a barrow.
And he called out loud
    As he rang his bell,
'Grannies to sell!
    Old grannies to sell!'

The neighbours said,
    As they passed them by,
'This poor old lady
    We will not buy.
He surely must be
    A mischievous man
To try for to sell
    His own dear Gran.'

'Besides,' said another,
    'If you ask me,
She'd be very small use
    That I can see.'
'You're right,' said a third,
    'And no mistake –
A very poor bargain
    She'd surely make.'

So Mr Tom Narrow
    He scratched his head,
And he sent his grandmother
    Back to bed;
And he rang his bell
    Through all the town
Till he sold his barrow
    For half a crown.

James Reeves

Zeke

Gnarly and bent and deaf's a post
Pore ole Ezekiel Purvis
Goeth crippin' slowly up the 'ill
To the Commoonion Survis.

And tappy tappy up the haisle
Goeth stick and brassy ferrule:
And Passon 'ath to stoopy down
An' 'olley in ees yerole.

L. A. G. Strong

Horrible Things

'What's the horriblest thing you've seen?'
Said Nell to Jean.

'Some grey-coloured, trodden-on plasticine;
On a plate, a left-over cold baked bean;
A cloak-room ticket numbered thirteen;
A slice of meat without any lean;
The smile of a spiteful fairy-tale queen;
A thing in the sea like a brown submarine;
A cheese fur-coated in brilliant green;
A bluebottle perched on a piece of sardine.
What's the horriblest thing *you've* seen?'
Said Jean to Nell.

'Your face, as you tell
Of all the horriblest things you've seen.'

Roy Fuller

'Be a Monster'

I am a frightful monster,
My face is cabbage green
And even with my mouth shut
My teeth can still be seen.
My finger-nails are like rats' tails
And very far from clean.

I cannot speak a language
But make a wailing sound
It could be any corner
You find me coming round.
Then, arms outspread
And eyeballs red,
I skim across the ground.

The girls scream out and scatter
From this girl-eating bat.
I usually catch a small one
Because her legs are fat;
Or it may be she's tricked by me
Wearing her grandpa's hat.

Roy Fuller

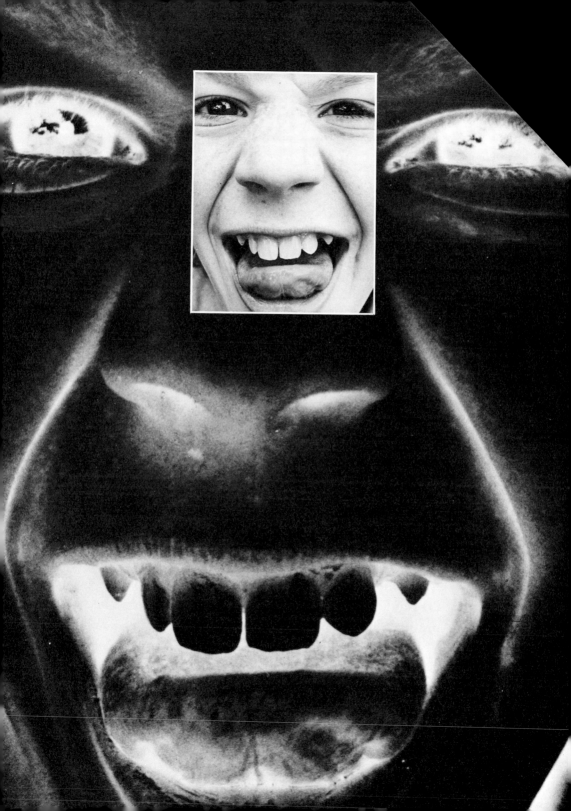

The Hairy Toe

Once there was a woman went out to pick beans,
and she found a Hairy Toe.
She took the Hairy Toe home with her,
and that night, when she went to bed,
the wind began to moan and groan.
Away off in the distance
she seemed to hear a voice crying,
'Where's my Hair-r-ry To-o-e?
Who's got my Hair-r-ry To-o-oe?'

54

The woman scrooched down,
way down under the covers,
and about that time
the wind appeared to hit the house,

smoosh,

and the old house creaked and cracked
like something was trying to get in.
The voice had come nearer,
almost at the door now,
and it said,
'Where's my Hair-r-ry To-o-oe?
Who's got my Hair-r-ry To-o-oe?'

The woman scrooched further down
under the covers
and pulled them tight around her head.

The wind growled around the house
like some big animal
and r-r-um-mbled
over the chimbley.
All at once she heard the door cr-r-a-ack
and Something slipped in
and began to creep over the floor.

The floor went
cre-e-eak, cre-e-eak
at every step that thing took towards her bed.
The woman could almost feel
it bending over her bed.
There in an awful voice it said:
'Where's my Hair-r-ry To-o-oe?
Who's got my Hair-r-ry To-o-oe?
You've got it!'

Traditional American

Moon-wind

There is no wind on the moon at all
   Yet things get blown about.
In utter utter stillness
   Your candle shivers out.

In utter utter stillness
   A giant marquee
Booms and flounders past you
   Like a swan at sea.

In utter utter stillness
   While you stand in the street
A squall of hens and cabbages
   Knocks you off your feet.

In utter utter stillness
   While you stand agog
A tearing twisting sheet of pond
   Clouts you with a frog.

A camp of caravans suddenly
   Squawks and takes off.
A ferris wheel bounds along the skyline
   Like a somersaulting giraffe.

Roots and foundations, nails and screws,
   Nothing can hold fast,
Nothing can resist the moon's
   Dead-still blast.

Ted Hughes

The Hag

The Hag is astride,
This night for to ride;
The Devil and she together:
Through thick and through thin,
Now out and then in,
Though ne'er so foul be the weather.

A thorn or a burr
She takes for a spur:
With a lash of a bramble she rides now,
Through brakes and through briars,
O'er ditches and mires,
She follows the Spirit that guides now.

No Beast for his food,
Dares now range the wood;
But hushed in his lair he lies lurking:
While mischiefs, by these,
On land and on seas,
At noon of night are a-working.

The storm will arise
And trouble the skies;
This night, and more for the wonder,
The ghost from the tomb
Affrighted shall come,
Called out by the clap of the thunder.

Robert Herrick

A Charm against the Toothache

Venerable Mother Toothache
Climb down from your white battlements,
Stop twisting in your yellow fingers
The fourfold rope of nerves;
And tomorrow I will give you a tot of whisky
To hold in your cupped hands,
A garland of anise-flowers,
And three cloves like nails.

And tell the attendant gnomes
It is time to knock off now,
To shoulder their little pick-axes,
Their cold chisels and drills,
And you may mount by a silver ladder
Into the sky, to grind
In the cracked polished mortar
Of the hollow moon.

By the lapse of warm waters,
And the poppies nodding like red coals,
The paths on the granite mountains,
And the plantation of my dreams.

John Heath-Stubbs

Traveller's Curse After Misdirection

May they stumble, stage by stage
On an endless pilgrimage,
Dawn and dusk, mile after mile,
At each and every step, a stile;
At each and every step withal
May they catch their feet and fall;
At each and every fall they take
May a bone within them break;
And may the bone that breaks within
Not be, for variation's sake,
Now rib, now thigh, now arm, now shin,
But always, without fail, THE NECK.

Robert Graves

Cowboy Song

I come from Salem County
   Where the silver melons grow,
Where the wheat is sweet as an angel's feet
   And the zithering zephyrs blow.
I walk the blue bone-orchard
   In the apple-blossom snow,
When the teasy bees take their honeyed ease
   And the marmalade moon hangs low.

My Maw sleeps prone on the prairie
   In a boulder eiderdown,
Where the pickled stars in their little jam-jars
   Hang in a hoop to town.
I haven't seen Paw since a Sunday
   In eighteen seventy-three
When he packed his snap in a bitty mess-trap
   And said he'd be home by tea.

Fled is my fancy sister
   All weeping like the willow,
And dead is the brother I loved like no other
   Who once did share my pillow.
I fly the florid water
   Where run the seven geese round,
O the townsfolk talk to see me walk
   Six inches off the ground.

Across the map of midnight
   I trawl the turning sky,
In my green glass the salt fleets pass
   The moon her fire-float by.
The girls go gay in the valley
   When the boys come down from the farm,
Don't run, my joy, from a poor cowboy,
   I won't do you no harm.

The bread of my twentieth birthday
   I buttered with the sun,
Though I sharpen my eyes with lovers' lies
   I'll never see twenty-one.
Light is my shirt with lilies,
   And lined with lead my hood,
On my face as I pass is a plate of brass,
   And my suit is made of wood.

Charles Causley

Angel Hill

A sailor came walking down Angel Hill,
He knocked on my door with a right good will,
With a right good will he knocked on my door.
He said, 'My friend, we have met before.'
  No, never, said I.

He searched my eye with a sea-blue stare
And he laughed aloud on the Cornish air,
On the Cornish air he laughed aloud
And he said, 'My friend, you have grown too proud.'
  No, never, said I.

'In war we swallowed the bitter bread
And drank of the brine,' the sailor said.
'We took of the bread and we tasted the brine
As I bound your wounds and you bound mine.'
        No, never, said I.

'By day and night on the diving sea
We whistled to sun and moon,' said he.
'Together we whistled to moon and sun
And vowed our stars should be as one.'
        No, never, said I.

'And now,' he said, 'that the war is past
I come to your hearth and home at last.
I come to your home and hearth to share
Whatever fortune waits me there.'
        No, never, said I.

'I have no wife nor son,' he said,
'Nor pillow on which to lay my head,
No pillow have I, nor wife nor son,
Till you shall give to me my own.'
        No, never, said I.

His eye it flashed like a lightning-dart
And still as a stone then stood my heart.
My heart as a granite stone was still
And he said, 'My friend, but I think you will.'
        No, never, said I.

The sailor smiled and turned in his track
And shifted the bundle on his back
And I heard him sing as he strolled away,
'You'll send and you'll fetch me one fine day.'
        No, never, said I.

Charles Causley

Emperors of the Island

There is the story of a deserted island
where five men walked down to the bay.

The story of the island is
that three men would two men slay.

Three men dug two graves in the sand,
three men stood on the sea wet rock,
three shadows moved away.

There is the story of a deserted island
where three men walked down to the bay.

The story of this island is
that two men would one man slay.

Two men dug one grave in the sand,
two men stood on the sea wet rock,
two shadows moved away.

There is the story of a deserted island
where two men walked down to the bay.

The story of this island is
that one man would one man slay.

One man dug one grave in the sand,
one man stood on the sea wet rock,
one shadow moved away.

There is the story of a deserted island
where four ghosts walked down to the bay.

The story of this island is
that four ghosts would one man slay.

Four ghosts dug one grave in the sand,
four ghosts stood on the sea wet rock;
five ghosts moved away.

Dannie Abse

After Ever Happily

or The Princess and the Woodcutter*

And they both lived happily ever after . . .
The wedding was held in the palace. Laughter
Rang to the roof as a loosened rafter
Crashed down and squashed the chamberlain flat –
And how the wedding guests chuckled at that!
'You, with your horny indelicate hands,
Who drop your haitches and call them 'ands,
Who cannot afford to buy her a dress,
How dare you presume to pinch our princess –
Miserable woodcutter, uncombed, unwashed!'
Were the chamberlain's words (before he was squashed).
'Take her,' said the Queen, who had a soft spot
For woodcutters. 'He's strong and he's handsome. Why
    not?'
'What rot!' said the King, but he dare not object;
The Queen wore the trousers – that's as you'd expect.
Said the chamberlain, usually meek and inscrutable,
'A princess and a woodcutter? The match is unsuitable.'
Her dog barked its welcome again and again,
As they splashed to the palace through puddles of rain.
And the princess sighed, 'Till the end of my life!'
'Darling,' said the woodcutter, 'will you be my wife?'
He knew all his days he could love no other,
So he nursed her to health with some help from his
    mother,
And lifted her, horribly hurt, from her tumble.
A woodcutter, watching, saw the horse stumble.
As she rode through the woods, a princess in her prime
On a dapple-grey horse . . . Now, to finish my rhyme,
I'll start it properly: Once upon a time –

* This is a love story from the Middle Ages. The poet obviously knew his
    subject-matter backwards.

Ian Serraillier

First Day at School

A millionbillionwillion miles from home
Waiting for the bell to go. (To go where?)
Why are they all so big, other children?
So noisy? So much at home they
must have been born in uniform
Lived all their lives in playgrounds
Spent the years inventing games
that don't let me in. Games
that are rough, that swallow you up.

And the railings.
All around, the railings.
Are they to keep out wolves and monsters?
Things that carry off and eat children?
Things you don't take sweets from?
Perhaps they're to stop us getting out
Running away from the lessins. Lessin.
What does a lessin look like?
Sounds small and slimy.
They keep them in glassrooms.
Whole rooms made out of glass. Imagine.

I wish I could remember my name
Mummy said it would come in useful.
Like wellies. When there's puddles.
Yellowwellies. I wish she was here.
I think my name is sewn on somewhere
Perhaps the teacher will read it for me.
Tea-cher. The one who makes the tea.

Roger McGough

Cold Feet

They have all gone across
They are all turning to see
They are all shouting 'come on'
They are all waiting for me.

I look through the gaps in the footway
And my heart shrivels with fear,
For far below the river is flowing
So quick and so cold and so clear.

And all that there is between it
And me falling down there is this:
A few wooden planks – not very thick –
And between each, a little abyss.

The holes get right under my sandals.
I can see straight through to the rocks,
And if I don't look, I can feel it,
Just there, through my shoes and my socks.

Suppose my feet and my legs withered up
And slipped through the slats like a rug?
Suppose I suddenly went very thin
Like the baby that slid down the plug?

I know that it cannot happen
But suppose that it did, what then?
Would they be able to find me
And take me back home again?

They have all gone across
They are all waiting to see
They are all shouting 'come on' —
But they'll have to carry me.

Brian Lee

67

529 1983

Absentmindedly,
sometimes,
I lift the receiver
And dial my own number.

(What revelations,
I think then,
If only
I could get through to myself.)

Gerda Mayer

Rain

The lights are all on, though it's just past midday,
There are no more indoor games we can play,
No one can think of anything to say,
It rained all yesterday, it's raining today,
It's grey outside, inside me it's grey.

I stare out of the window, fist under my chin,
The gutter leaks drips on the lid of the dustbin,
When they say 'cheer up', I manage a grin,
I draw a fish on the glass with a sail-sized fin,
It's sodden outside, and it's damp within.

Matches, bubbles and papers pour into the drains,
Clouds smother the sad laments from the trains,
Grandad says it brings on his rheumatic pains,
The moisture's got right inside of my brains,
It's raining outside, inside me it rains.

Brian Lee

maggie and millie and molly and may
went down to the beach (to play one day)

and maggie discovered a shell that sang
so sweetly she couldn't remember her troubles, and

milly befriended a stranded star
whose rays five languid fingers were;

and molly was chased by a horrible thing
which raced sideways while blowing bubbles; and

may came home with a smooth white stone
as small as a world and as large as alone.

For whatever we lose (like a you or a me)
it's always ourselves we find in the sea

e. e. cummings

Horrible Song

The Crow is a wicked creature
    Crooked in every feature.
Beware, beware of the Crow!
When the bombs burst, he laughs, he shouts;
When guns go off, he roundabouts;
When the limbs start to fly and the blood starts to flow
    Ho Ho Ho
    He sings the Song of the Crow.

The Crow is a sudden creature
    Thievish in every feature.
Beware, beware of the Crow!
When the sweating farmers sleep
He levers the jewels from the heads of their sheep.
Die in a ditch, your own will go,
    Ho Ho Ho
    While he sings the Song of the Crow.

The Crow is a subtle creature
    Cunning in every feature.
Beware, beware of the Crow!
When sick folk tremble on their cots
He sucks their souls through the chimney pots,
They're dead and gone before they know,
    Ho Ho Ho
    And he sings the Song of the Crow.

The Crow is a lusty creature
    Gleeful in every feature.
Beware, beware of the Crow!
If he can't get your liver, he'll find an old rat
Or highway hedgehog hammered flat,
Any old rubbish to make him grow,
    Ho Ho Ho
    While he sings the Song of the Crow.

The Crow is a hardy creature
    Fire-proof in every feature.
Beware, beware of the Crow!
When Mankind's blasted to kingdom come
The Crow will dance and hop and drum
And into an old thigh-bone he'll blow
    Ho Ho Ho
    Singing the Song of the Crow.

Ted Hughes

Robin

With a bonfire throat,
Legs of twig
A dark brown coat,
The inspector robin
Comes where I dig.

Military man
With a bright eye
And a wooden leg,
He must scrounge and beg
Now the summer's by:

Beg at the doors,
Scrounge in the gardens,
While daylight lessens
And the grass glistens
And the ground hardens.

The toads have their vaults,
The squirrels their money,
The swifts their journey:
For him the earth's anger,
The taste of hunger.

And his unfrightened song
For the impending snows
Is also for the rose,
And for the great armada
And the Phoenician trader,
And the last missile raider –
It's the only one he knows.

Hal Summers

Night Crow

When I saw that clumsy crow
Flap from a wasted tree,
A shape in the mind rose up:
Over the gulfs of dream
Flew a tremendous bird
Further and further away
Into a moonless black,
Deep in the brain, far back.

Theodore Roethke

October garden:
At the top of the tree
A thrush stabs an apple.

November Story

The evening had caught cold;
Its eyes were blurred.
It had a dripping nose
And its tongue was furred.

I sat in a warm bar
After the day's work;
November snuffled outside,
Greasing the sidewalk.

But soon I had to go
Out into the night
Where shadows prowled the alleys,
Hiding from the light.

But light shone at the corner
On the pavement where
A man had fallen over
Or been knocked down there.

His legs on the slimed concrete
Were splayed out wide;
He had been propped against a lamp-post;
His head lolled to one side.

A victim of crime or accident,
An image of fear,
He remained quite motionless
As I drew near.

Then a thin voice startled silence
From a doorway close by
Where an urchin hid from the wind:
'Spare a penny for the guy!'

I gave the boy some money
And hastened on.
A voice called, 'Thank you guv'nor!'
And the words upon

The wincing air seemed strange –
So hoarse and deep –
As if the guy had spoken
In his restless sleep.

Vernon Scannell

Fireworks

They rise like sudden fiery flowers
    That burst upon the night,
Then fall to earth in burning showers
    Of crimson, blue, and white.

Like buds too wonderful to name,
    Each miracle unfolds,
And catherine-wheels begin to flame
    Like whirling marigolds.

Rockets and Roman candles make
    An orchard of the sky,
Whence magic trees their petals shake
    Upon each gazing eye.

James Reeves

November Morning:
A whiff of cordite
Caught in the leaf mould.

Carol

The Palm Court Lounge is snug and warm
There's Scotch on every table
It's not our fault it's not so hot
Next door in the hotel stable

The passengers are drunk tonight
The crew have cash to burn
So who will hear the drowning man
We've left ten miles astern?

Let's all go down the Motorway
And see who's first at Chester
Let's all forget that scruffy dog
We knocked for six at Leicester

O we're all right and so is Jack
(He's underneath the table)
It's not our fault it's not so hot
Next door in the hotel stable

God rest us merry, Gentlemen,
This is no time for sorrow
Because ten thousand refugees
Will get no grub tomorrow

The Landlord smiles and lays the bill
Quite gently on the table
The man who'll pay has just been born
Next door in an ice-cold stable.

Ronald Deadman

The Computer's First Christmas Card

jollymerry
hollyberry
jollyberry
merryholly
happyjolly
jollyjelly
jellybelly
bellymerry
hollyheppy
jollyMolly
marryJerry
merryHarry
hoppyBarry
heppyJarry
boppyheppy
berryjorry
jorryjelly
moppyjelly
Mollymerry
Jerryjolly
bellyboppy
jorryhoppy
hollymoppy
Barrymerry
Jarryhappy
happyboppy
boppyjolly
jollymerry
merrymerry
merrymerry
merryChris
asmerryasa
Chrismerry
asMERRYCHR
YSANTHEMUM

Edwin Morgan

TV

In the coloured world of home
there's a greyish oblong hole;
and it's the only thing that
moves among the furniture.

Somewhere past the couch tiny
clouds and horses spring into
view and disappear before
they get to the window-sill.

Though these things and beings are
so small, their noise is human.
Passing empty rooms, you hear
gun-shots and angry talking.

Even when there is no one
to see or hear it, this life
in the curved glass probably
goes on just the same. Who knows?

Our universe began in
a concentrated atom.
So does this screen of shadows
when you first switch on the knob.

It also ends like that as
you switch the other way, though
first the sound dies, and all yell,
but cannot make themselves heard.

Roy Fuller

Postscript on the arrival of colour

In the greyish world of home
there's a coloured oblong hole;
and naturally we all sit
with our red eyes glued on it.

Farm Child

Look at this village boy, his head is stuffed
With all the nests he knows, his pockets with flowers,
Snail-shells and bits of glass, the fruit of hours
Spent in the fields by thorn and thistle tuft.
Look at his eyes, see the harebell hiding there;
Mark how the sun has freckled his smooth face
Like a finch's egg under that bush of hair
That dares the wind, and in the mixen now
Notice his poise: from such unconscious grace
Earth breeds and beckons to the stubborn plough.

R. S. Thomas

My Bonny Black Bess

Dick Turpin bold! Dick, hie away,
Was the cry of my pals, who were startled, I guess,
For the pistols were levelled, the bullets whizzed by,
As I leapt on the back of Black Bess.
Three Officers mounted, led forward the chase,
Resolv'd in the capture to share;
But I smil'd on their efforts, tho' swift was their pace,
As I urg'd on my bonny Black Mare.
So when I've a bumper, what can I do less,
   Than the memory drink of my bonny Black Bess?

Hark away, hark away! still onward they press,
As we saw by the glimmer of morn,
Tho' many a mile on the back of Black Bess,
That night I was gallantly borne;
Hie over, my pet, the fatigue I must bear
Well clear'd! never falter for breath,
Hark forward, my girl, my bonny Black Mare,
We speed it for life or for death.
But when I've a bumper, what can I do less,
   Than the memory drink of my bonny Black Bess?

The spires of York now burst on my view,
But the chimes, they were ringing her knell,
Halt! Halt! my brave mare, they no longer pursue,
She halted, she staggered, she fell!
Her breathing was o'er, all was hushed as the grave,
Alas! poor Black Bess, once my pride,
Her heart she had burst, her rider to save,
For Dick Turpin, she lived, and she died.
Then the memory drink of my bonny Black Bess,
Hurrah for poor bonny Black Bess!

Anon

Reindeer

I wriggled silently through the swamp,
carrying bow and arrow in my mouth.
The marsh was broad, the water icy cold,
and there was no cover in sight.

Slowly, soaked, invisible,
I crawled within range.
The reindeer were eating;
they grazed the juicy moss
without concern,
till my arrow sank
tremblingly deep
into the bull's side.

Terrified, the unsuspecting herd
hastily scattered,
and vanished at the sharpest trot
to shielding hills.

Aua

The Mouse's Invitation Cards

'Come at seven,' 'Come at nine,'
'Come whenever you want.'
On the shelf the printed cards
Seem kind in their intent.

But the mouse will always stay at home,
He will never venture out,
No matter how the cards insist
Friends are all about.

One's from a cat, one's from an owl,
And both are intent
To draw him from his nest and then
Have him where they want.

Brian Patten

The Owl's Trick

In a place, dark, disguised,
A place not fit for our eyes,
In a hollow, ancient tree
The owl speaks philosophically:

'About my feet are swarms of mice
And I can easily leave them there.
From their feet I've ripped their toes,
And now they'll not go anywhere.

'I eat them slowly at my ease,
I pick and choose them as I please.
The fattest one I let digest
Before indulging in the next.

'I bring them corn into my croft,
It keeps them alive and it keeps them soft.
Before this idea came to me
They were nimble and ran away.

'Now I've neatly torn the paws from each
And they panic forever within my reach.
This trick mankind viewed with alarm –
And then invented the Cattle-farm.'

Brian Patten

The Game of Life

Have you been in sight of heaven
Far ahead on ninety-seven,
Then swirled the dice and thrown a one,
Slid down a snake and flopped upon
Some square like sixty-three?

And then what made you even madder
Seen your sister climb a ladder
To eighty-four from twenty-eight
And felt a sudden rush of hate
As she smirked with glee?

And have you thought she counted out
(So as to miss a snake's dread snout)
A few too many squares – and stayed
Quiet because you were afraid
Or just through leniency?

If so, you will already know
How bitter life can be; and show
Upon your countenance no sign
Except perhaps a smile benign.
And shake on doggedly.

Roy Fuller

The Road not Taken

Two roads diverged in a yellow wood,
And sorry I could not travel both
And be one traveller, long I stood
And looked down one as far as I could
To where it bent in the undergrowth;

Then took the other, as just as fair,
And having perhaps the better claim,
Because it was grassy and wanted wear;
Though as for that the passing there
Had worn them really about the same,

And both that morning equally lay
In leaves no step had trodden black.
Oh, I kept the first for another day!
Yet knowing how way leads on to way,
I doubted if I should ever come back.

I shall be telling this with a sigh
Somewhere ages and ages hence:
Two roads diverged in a wood, and I –
I took the one less travelled by,
And that has made all the difference.

Robert Frost

The Apple-raid

Darkness came early, though not yet cold;
Stars were strung on the telegraph wires;
Street lamps spilled pools of liquid gold;
The breeze was spiced with garden fires.

That smell of burnt leaves, the early dark,
Can still excite me but not as it did
So long ago when we met in the park –
Myself, John Peters and David Kidd.

We moved out of town to the district where
The lucky and wealthy had their homes
With garages, gardens, and apples to spare
Ripely clustered in the trees' green domes.

We chose the place we meant to plunder
And climbed the wall and dropped down to
The secret dark. Apples crunched under
Our feet as we moved through the grass and dew.

The clusters on the lower boughs of the tree
Were easy to reach. We stored the fruit
In pockets and jerseys until all three
Boys were heavy with their tasty loot.

Safe on the other side of the wall
We moved back to town and munched as we went.
I wonder if David remembers at all
That little adventure, the apples' fresh scent.

Strange to think that he's fifty years old,
That tough little boy with scabs on his knees;
Stranger to think that John Peters lies cold
In an orchard in France beneath apple trees.

Vernon Scannell

The Spitfire on the Northern Line

Harry was an uncle. I saw him twice.
Both times he was a sailor home from war.
First, he arrived one morning, thumped the door,
Annoying old Ma Brown on the second floor,
And brought me two string-bags click-full of marbles.
In the grey light of that wartime dawn we lay
On the cold lino, rumbling zig-zag balls
Of colour to all corners of the room,
Until Ma Brown banged up at us with her broom.
I felt like a god in heaven, playing with thunder.
The second time, we went by Underground
To see his mother, my grandma. In all
That packed and rocking tube-train; down we sat
Together on the dirty wooden slats
Between the feet of passengers, and began
To build a Spitfire. He would send me off
Toddling with tininess against the sway
Of the train to fetch a propeller, then the wheels,
While like a Buddha crosslegged, all in blue,
He sat and bashed a nail or sank a screw.
And before the eyes of all, a Spitfire grew
And finally (a stop before the Angel)
He cried 'It's finished!' and the whole coachful
Shouted 'Hooray!'
                    Never, never again
Did I see Harry. Somewhere he was killed
And they slipped his body softly to the sea.
Thousands died that war. Most, like Harry,
Not distinguished by the enemies gunned down,
But remembered by some child.
                                I see it still,
That Spitfire on the Northern Line, nose-up,
Blotched with its camouflage, and gleaming bright,
And all those faces laughing with delight.

Brian James

The Rescue

The boy climbed up into the tree.
The tree rocked; so did he.
He was trying to rescue a cat,
A cushion of a cat, from where it sat
In a high crutch of branches, mewing
As though to say to him, 'Nothing doing,'

Whenever he shouted, 'Come on, come down.'
So up he climbed, and the whole town
Lay at his feet, round him the leaves
Fluttered like a lady's sleeves,
And the cat sat, and the wind blew so
That he would have flown had he let go.
At last he was high enough to scoop
That fat white cushion or nincompoop
And tuck her under his arm, and turn
To go down –
                    But oh! he began to learn
How high he was, how hard it would be
Having come up with four limbs, to go down with three.
His heart-beats knocked as he tried to think:
He would put the cat in a lower chink –
She appealed to him with a cry of alarm
And put her eighteen claws in his arm.
So he stayed looking down for a minute or so
To the good ground so far below.
When the minute started he saw it was hard;
When it ended he couldn't move a yard.

So there he was stuck, in the failing light
And the wind rising with the coming of the night.
His father! He shouted for all he was worth.
His father came nearer: 'What on earth –?'
'I've got the cat up here but I'm stuck.'
'Hold on. . . . ladder . . .', he heard. Oh, luck!
How lovely behind the branches tossing
The globes at the pedestrian crossing
And the big fluorescent lamps glowed
Mauve-green on the main road.
But his father didn't come back, didn't come;
His little fingers were going numb.

The cat licked them as though to say
'Are you feeling cold? I'm O.K.'
He wanted to cry, he would count ten first,
But just as he was ready to burst,
A torch came and his father and mother
And a ladder and the dog and his younger brother.
Up on a big branch stood his father,
His mother came to the top of the ladder,
His brother stood on a lower rung,
The dog sat still and put out its tongue.
From one to another the cat was handed
And afterwards she was reprimanded.
After that it was easy, though the wind blew:
The parents came down, the boy came too
From the ladder, the lower branch and the upper
And all of them went indoors to supper,
And the tree rocked and the moon sat
In the branches like a white cat.

Hal Summers

Late Home

I looked up – the sun had gone down
Though it was there a minute before
And the light had grown terribly thin
And no one played by the shore
Of the lake, now empty, and still;
And I heard the park-keepers shout
As they cycled around the paths . . .
'Closing, closing . . . everyone out . . . '

Then I panicked and started to run,
Leaving all of my friends behind
(I could hear their cries in the bushes –
It was me they were trying to find)
But they had the burn and the minnows,
The rope, the slide, the shrubbery track,
And the trees where a thrush was singing,
And I had the long road back –

The road that led, empty and straight,
Down under the tall grey flats
Where the lights were on, and the tellies,
And old ladies were putting out cats:
I ran past them, without looking round
As though I'd committed a crime:
At six they'd said 'Just half an hour'
And *now* – oh, what was the time?

How could it have gone already?
Something must be, it *must* be, wrong –
I've only just come out – and why
Does getting back take me so long?
I can't be late – or if I am,
It's the fault of the sun or the moon.
When the dentist's takes an eternity,
How are happy things over so soon?

So I stopped and asked, 'Please mister . . . '
And his left wrist came slowly round
And he peered at his watch and shook it
And said 'Blast, it's never been wound up.'
But the next man hauled his watch up,
Like a lead sinker on a line,
Clicked open the front, and boomed out,
'Right now, child, it's five to nine'.

There's a great big gap in between
The way things are, the way things seem,
And I dropped down it then, like you do
When you shoot back to life from a dream.
I stood there and muttered 'It can't be –
His watch must be wrong' – then, aghast –
'This time, I'll *really* be for it.
If it isn't a whole two hours fast.'

But I got my legs going again
And ran, gulping in red-hot air,
Through back-streets where no one knew me,
Till I came out in the Town Square.
But when I looked at the shining face
And I heard the cheerful chimes
Of the Town Hall clock – then every hope
Drained away, as it struck nine times.

Two hours late . . . *two hours late* –
Perhaps they've called out the police
Two hours late . . . who, all in a line,
Are combing the waste ground, piece by piece;
While *they* all stand in our window
Anxious and angry and, when I'm seen,
Ready to frown and shout 'There he is',
'Come here you!', and 'Where's the child been?'

When I come round the corner and see them,
I'll limp, as though I'd a sprain,
Then whimper 'I didn't mean it' and
'I'll never ever go out, again . . .
How can I know that time's up,
When I'm enjoying myself such a lot?
I'm sorry – won't you take me back in?
Are you glad to see me, or not?'

. . . But later in bed, as I lay there
In the extraordinary light –
Filtering through the half-drawn curtain –
Of that silvery spellbound night,
I wondered just what *had* happened
To Time, for three hours in June:
If all of my life is as happy –
Will it all be over as soon?

Brian Lee

Legend

The blacksmith's boy went out with a rifle
and a black dog running behind.
Cobwebs snatched at his feet,
rivers hindered him,
thorn branches caught at his eyes to make him blind
and the sky turned into an unlucky opal,
but he didn't mind,
I can break branches, I can swim rivers, I can stare out any
   spider I meet,
said he to his dog and his rifle.

The blacksmith's boy went over the paddocks
with his old black hat on his head.
Mountains jumped in his way,
rocks rolled down on him,
and the old crow cried, You'll soon be dead.
And the rain came down like mattocks.
But he only said
I can climb mountains, I can dodge rocks, I can shoot an
   old crow any day,
and he went on over the paddocks.

When he came to the end of the day the sun began falling.
Up came the night ready to swallow him,
like the barrel of the gun,
like an old black hat,
like a black dog hungry to follow him.
Then the pigeon, the magpie and the dove began wailing
and the grass lay down to billow him.
His rifle broke, his hat flew away and his dog was gone
and the sun was falling.

But in front of the night the rainbow stood on a mountain,
just as his heart foretold.
He ran like a hare,
he climbed like a fox;
he caught it in his hands, the colour and the cold –
like a bar of ice, like the column of a fountain,

93

like a ring of gold.
The pigeon, the magpie and the dove flew to stare,
And the grass stood up again on the mountain.

The blacksmith's boy hung the rainbow on his shoulder
instead of his broken gun.
Lizards ran out to see,
snakes made way for him,
and the rainbow shone as brightly as the sun.
All the world said, Nobody is braver, nobody is bolder,
Nobody else has done
anything to equal it. He went home as bold as he could be
with the swinging rainbow on his shoulder.

Judith Wright

Index of Titles and First Lines

95

Oxford University Press, Walton Street, Oxford OX2 6DP

Oxford New York Toronto Delhi Bombay Calcutta Madras Karachi Petaling Jaya Singapore
Hong Kong Tokyo Nairobi Dar es Salaam Cape Town Melbourne Auckland

and associated companies in Berlin Ibadan

Oxford is a trade mark of Oxford University Press

Selection and arrangement © Oxford University Press, 1979 ISBN 0 19 834266 7

First published 1979
Reprinted 1981 (twice), 1983 (twice),
1984, 1986, 1987, 1990, 1991

Set in Great Britain by Fakenham Press Limited, Fakenham, Norfolk
Printed and bound in Hong Kong